Tongue Twister Challenge

700 Awesome Twisters Guaranteed to Tongue Tie You in No Time!

Laughing Lion

Free Audiobook versions of this and many other Laughing Lion books?
Sign up using the link below or scan the QR code with your phone.

bit.ly/3j3vmD2

CONTENTS

EASY PEASY 9

AVERAGE JOE 25

TWISTED 57

DOUBLE KNOT 79

SUPERCALI-TWISTED III

THE TOUGHEST 123

INTRODUCTION

Challenges can be tough, but not when you can do it with your friends and family. I hope the Tongue Twister Challenge will inspire you to do tricky things and find joy in it.

I wrote this book thinking of the times you share with your family after a busy day or on the weekend. Tongue twisters have been around for ages. I decided to make a game out of it to turn a simple gathering into a memorable one.

So, are you up for a good tongue-twisting, endless giggling, and mind-blowing challenge? This book is divided into levels, from short phrases to long sentences. And you are in for a surprise when you reach the end of the book. If you think you can, and I know you can, do the can-can, and start the challenge if you can.

HOW TO PLAY

For each level, say a number without looking at the book.

Find the number in the book and read the tongue twister.

You should be able to say it quickly for five times in one try.

If you can do it, you get a point.

If not, try your luck in your next turn.

The players will take turns doing the game.

Whoever gets the greatest number of points wins!

EASY PEASY

(less than 5 words)

Cooks cooks cupcakes quickly, Cook cooks cupcakes quickly

1. Hiccup teacup!

2. Swim, swam, swum!

3. Greek grapes.

4. Cheap Ship Trip

5. Higgledy-Piggedly!

6. Red lorry, yellow lorry.

7. Luke Luck likes lakes.

8. Cheap sheep soup.

9. Bad black bran bread.

10. Lovely lemon liniment.

11. Freshly-fried flying fish.

12. He threw three balls.

13. Rubber baby buggy bumpers

14. Sheena leads, Sheila needs.

15. World Wide Web

16. Seventy-seven benevolent elephants.

17. Santa's short suit shrunk.

18. Willy's real rear wheel

19. Black background, brown background.

20. Three short sword sheaths.

21. Rolling red wagons

22. Black back bat

23. Red Buick, blue Buick

24. Scissors sizzle, thistles sizzle.

25. Eddie edited it.

26. Thin grippy thick slippery.

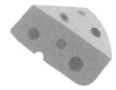 27. She sees cheese.

28. Swatch watch

29. Mummies make money.

30. Really leery, rarely Larry.

31. Red blood, green blood

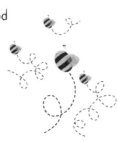

32. Busy buzzing bumble bees

33. Six shining cities.

34. Preshrunk silk shirts.

35. Red lolly, yellow lolly.

36. Knapsack strap.

37. Great gray goats

38. Clowns grow glowing crowns.

39. Red leather, yellow leather

40. Richard's wretched ratchet wrench.

41. Mallory's hourly salary.

42. Sweater weather, leather weather.

43. Unique New York

44. Thin sticks, thick bricks

45. Six thick thistle sticks.

46. Irish wristwatch

47. A real rare whale.

48. Some shun sunshine.

49. She sewed shirts seriously.

50. A queer quick questioning quiz.

51. Cross crossings cautiouslyl

52. Slim Sam slid sideways.

53. Yellow Yo-Yo's.

54. Silver thimbles.

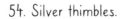

55. A black-backed bath brush.

56. Truly plural

57. A missing mixture measure.

58. Alice asks for axes

59. Ape Cakes, Grape Cakes.

60. Are our oars oak?

61. Chop shops stock chops.

62. Crisp crusts crackle crunchily

63. Do thick tinkers think?

64. Ex-disk jockey.

65. Freckle-faced Freddie fidgets.

66. Girl gargoyle, guy gargoyle.

67. Inchworms itching.

68. Kinky kite kits.

69. Lisa laughed listlessly.

70. June sheep sleep soundly.

71. Keenly cleaning copper kettles

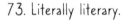

72. Mix, Miss Mix!

73. Literally literary.

74. Local yokel jokes.

75. Moose noshing much mush.

76. Much mashed mushrooms.

77. Nick knits Nixon's knickers.

78. Nine nice night nymphs.

79. Norse myths.

80. Peggy Bobcock's mummy.

81. Plague-bearing prairie dogs.

82. Please pay promptly.

83. Pooped purple pelicans.

84. Raise Ruth's red roof.

85. Reed Wade Road

86. Rex wrecks wet rocks.

87. Rudder valve reversals

88. Rush the washing, Russel!

89. Salty broccoli

90. Selfish shellfish..

91. Seth's sharp spacesuit shrank.

92. She had shoulder surgery

93. She sells Swiss sweets.

94. Shredded Swiss cheese.

95. Six crisp snacks

96. Six sharp smart sharks

97. Six short slow shepherds.

98. Spark plug car park.

99. Stagecoach stops.

100. Such a shapeless sash!

101. Supposed to be pistachio

102. Synonym cinnamon.

103. Tacky tractor trailer trucks.

104. The blue bluebird blinks.

105. The ex-egg examiner.

106. Thieves seize skis.

107. Three twigs twined tightly.

 108. Try fat flat flounders.

109. Twice we tripped toys.

110. Two toads, totally tired.

111. Valuable valley villas.

112. Zithers slither slowly south.

113. Zizzi's zippy zipper zips.

114. Which witch is which?

115. Cooks cook cupcakes quickly.

116. Six Czech cricket critics.

117. Daddy Draws Doors.

118. Black Rock Brain Lock.

119. Six sticky skeletons.

120. Friendly fleas and fireflies.

121. Broken blue crayon

122. Burger burglar

123. Click, clap, pluck

124. Chill, Shake, Serve

125. Cheap Sheep Sheets

126. Cracker rapper

127. Crash Quiche Course

128. Darla's dollars

129. Darn dawn dog gone!

130. Faith's face cloth

131. Free Ritz wristwatch.

132. Freshly fried fresh flesh

133. Friskies frisbee

134. Loyal royal lawyer

135. Midget minute

136. Mumbling, bumbling. Bumbling, mumbling.

137. Peter Rabbit radish robber

138. Plaid pleated pants

139. Purple paper people

140. Shine my city shoes

141. Thirty-six thick silk threads

142. Swift shift

143. Upper roller, lower roller

144. Thunder sunders thick sticks.

145. Dick kicks sticky bricks.

146. Children chuckle cheerily.

147. Charles Dickens has chickens.

AVERAGE JOE

(5 to 10 words)

Singing Sammy sung songs on sinking sand.

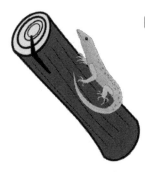

1. Loopy lizards lying lazily aloft a little lane of logs.

2. Clean clams crammed in clean cans.

3. Lonely lowland llamas are ladylike.

4. A slimy snake slithered down the sandy Sahara.

5. Gale's great glass globe glows green.

6. A noisy noise annoys an oyster.

7. Does this shop sport short socks with spots?

8. Which wristwatches are

Swiss wristwatches?

9. On a lazy laser raiser

lies a laser ray eraser.

10. The sun shines on

the shop signs.

11. Six sick slick slim

sycamore saplings.

12. Around the rugged rocks the

ragged rascals ran.

13. Double bubble gum, bubbles double.

14. I scream, you scream,

we all scream for ice cream!

15. Tommy Tucker tried totie Tammy's Turtles tie.

16. Jolly juggling jesters jauntily
juggled jingling jacks.

17. He misses her Swiss miss.
Her Swiss miss misses him.

18. A loyal warrior will rarely
worry why we rule.

19. Two tried and true tired.

20. How can a clam cram in
a clean cream can?

21. Send toast to ten tense
stout saints' ten tall tents.

22. Seth at Sainsbury's sells
thick socks.

23. Roberta ran rings around
the Roman ruins.

24. Wayne went to Wales

to watch walruses.

25. Six sleek swans swam

swiftly southwards

26. He threw three free throws.

27. Gobbling gargoyles gobbled

gobbling goblins.

28. A big black bug bit a big black

dog on his big black nose!

29. Ann and Andy's anniversary

is in April.

30. Thirty-three thirsty, thundering thoroughbreds thumped Mr.

Thurber on Thursday.

31. Four furious friends fought

for the phone.

32. Tie twine to three tree twigs.

33. Green glass globes glow greenly.

34. The queen in green screamed.

35. Six slimy snails sailed silently.

36. I thought, I thought of thinking

of thanking you.

37. Seven slick slimy snakes

slowly sliding southward.

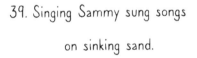

38. The great Greek grape

growers grow great Greek grapes.

39. Singing Sammy sung songs

on sinking sand.

40. Near an ear, a nearer ear,

a nearly eerie ear.

41. On a lazy laser raiser

lies a laser ray eraser.

42. Does your sport shop stock short socks with spots?

43. Little Mike left his bike

like Tike at Spike's.

44. Fresh French fried fly fritters

45. Wow, race winners really

want red wine right away!

46. I'll chew and chew until my jaws drop.

47. Chester Cheetah chews a chunk

of cheep cheddar cheese.

48. Two tiny tigers take two

taxis to town.

49. Sounding by sound is a sound
method of sounding sounds.

50. This is the sixth zebra
snoozing thoroughly.

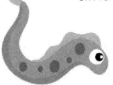

51. I eat eel while you peel eel.

52. I wish you were a fish in my dish.

53. Dust is a disk's worst enemy.

54. She said she should sit!

55. She says she shall sew a sheet.

56. A gazillion gigantic grapes gushed
gradually giving gophers gooey guts.

57. Five frantic frogs fled
from fifty fierce fishes.

58. I'm a sock cutter and I cut socks.

59. Silly sheep weep and sleep.

60. Thirty-three thousand people think that Thursday is their thirtieth birthday.

61. Shut up the shutters and sit in the shop.

62. Rattle your bottles in Rollocks' van.

63. Bake big batches of bitter brown bread.

64. Crush grapes, grapes crush, crush grapes.

65. Elizabeth has eleven elves in her elm tree.

66. Her whole right hand really hurts.

67. A lump of red leather,

a red leather lump

68. Nat the bat swat at Matt the gnat.

69. Craig Quinn's quick trip

to Crabtree Creek.

70. No nose knows like a gnome's nose knows.

71. A bloke's bike back brake black broke.

72. She stood by Burgess's fish sauce

shop welcoming him in.

73. A big black bear sat on

a big black bug.

74. Ripe white wheat reapers

reap ripe white wheat right.

75. Each Easter Eddie eats

eighty Easter eggs.

76. She slits the sheet she sits on.

77. Twelve twins twirled twelve twigs.

78. The soldier's shoulder surely hurts!

79. She sees seas slapping shores.

80. Never trouble about trouble

until trouble troubles you!

81. Blue glue gun, green glue gun.

82. Five fat friars frying flat fish.

83. The big black bug's blood ran blue.

84. Miss Smith's fish-sauce shop seldom sells shellfish.

85. Six sick sea-serpents swam the seven seas.

86. Tim, the thin twin tinsmith.

87. Plain bun, plum bun, bun without plum.

88. Slick slim slippers sliding south.

89. People pledging plenty of pennies.

90. The little red lorry went down Limuru road.

91. Flies fly but a fly flies.

92. My mommy makes me muffins on Mondays.

93. Lotty licks lollies lolling in the lobby.

94. Sly Sam sips Sally's soup.

95. Nine nimble noblemen nibble nuts.

96. Barbara burned the
brown bread badly.

97. While trying to whistle,
Christopher Twistle
twisted his tongue.

98. Quinn's twin sisters sing tongue twisters.

99. A bootblack blacks boots with a black blacking brush.

100. Six silly sisters sell silk to six
sickly seniors.

101. Bonnie Bliss blows big beautiful
blue bubbles.

102. Shy Sheila shakes soft shimmering silks.

103. The two twenty-two tore

through town.

104. I go by a Blue Goose bus.

105. Let little Nellie run a little.

106. Don't run along the wrong lane

107. The dude dropped in at the

Dewdrop Inn.

108. I never felt felt that felt

like that felt felt

109. Does the wristwatch shop shut soon?

110. When does the wristwatch strap

shop shut?

111. The wild wind whipped Whit from the wharf.

112. We surely shall see the sun shine soon.

113. A cupcake cook in a cupcake

cook's cap cooks cupcakes.

114. A dozen dim ding-dongs.

115. A fat-free fruit float.

116. A gentle judge judges justly.

117. A nurse anesthetist unearthed a nest.

118. A pack of pesky pixies.

 119. A quick witted cricket critic.

120. Ah shucks, six stick shifts stuck shut!

121. Awful old Ollie oils oily autos.

122. Brad's big black bath brush broke

123. Brent Spence Bridge

Clay Wade Bailey Bridge

124. Come kick six sticks quick.

125. Cedar shingles should be shaved

and saved.

126. Chocolate chip cookies

in a copper coffee cup.

127. Dear mother,

give your other udder to my other brother.

128. Don't pamper damp scamp tramps

that camp under ramp lamps.

129. East Fife Four, Forfar Five

130. Eight great gray geese grazing gaily into Greece.

131. Ere her ear hears her err,

here ears err here

132. Extinct insects' instincts, extant

insects' instincts.

133. False Frank fled Flo Friday.

134. Fat frogs flying past fast.

135. Few free fruit flies fly

from flames.

136. Flee from fog to fight flu fast!

137. Four free-flow pipes flow freely.

138. Fran feeds fish fresh fish food.

139. Fred fed Ted bread, and Ted

fed Fred bread.

140. Friendly Frank flips fine flapjacks.

141. I was born on a pirate ship.

142. If he slipped, should she slip?

143. Ike ships ice chips in ice chips ships.

144. Jack's nap sack strap snapped.

145. Listen to the local yokel yodel.

146. Larry sent the latter a letter later.

147. Kris Kringle carefully crunched candy canes

148. Tom threw Tim three thumbtacks.

149. Lesser leather never weathered wetter weather better.

150. Lily ladles little Letty's lentil soup.

151. Many an anemone sees an enemy anemone

152. No shark shares swordfish steak.

153. No shipshape ships shop stocks shop-soiled shirts

154. Octopus ocular optics. and
a cat snaps a rat's paxwax.

155. Pail of ale aiding ailing Al's travails.

156. Paul, please pause for proper applause.

157. Roland road in a
Rolls Royce.

158. Roofs of mushrooms rarely mush
too much.

159. Sinful Caesar sipped his snifter, seized his knees and
sneezed

160. Selfish sharks sell shut shellfish.

161. Shelter for six sick scenic sightseers.

162. Sherman shops at cheap chop suey shops.

163. Shy Shelly says she shall sew sheets.

164. Sam's shop stocks short spotted socks.

165. Six shimmering sharks sharply

striking shins.

166. Six shy shavers sheared six shy sheep.

167. Six slippery snails, slid slowly seaward.

168. Six twin screwed steel steam cruisers.

169. The boot black bought the black

boot back

170. The cat crept into the creepy crypt and crept out.

171. The fickle finger of fate flips

fat frogs flat.

172. The fuzzy bee buzzed the buzzy

busy beehive.

173. The hare's ear heard ere the hare heeded.

174. The myth of Miss Muffet.

175. The ochre ogre ogled the poker.

176. The quack quit asking quick questions.

177. The queen coined quick clipped quips.

178. The two-twenty-two train tore through the tunnel.

179. Thelma sings the theme song.

180. There goes one tough top cop!

181. There was a minimum of cinnamon in the aluminum pan.

182. They both, though, have thirty-three thick thimbles to thaw.

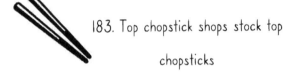

183. Top chopstick shops stock top chopsticks

184. Twelve standard stainless steel twin screw cruisers.

185. Two dozen double damask dinner napkins.

186. Wally Winkle wriggles his white, wrinkled wig.

187. Which rich wicked witch wished the wicked wish?

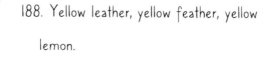

188. Yellow leather, yellow feather, yellow lemon.

189. A happy hippo hopped and hiccupped.

190. A snake sneaks to seek a snack.

191. The big bug bit the little beetle.

192. Betty's big bunny bobbled by the blueberry bush.

193. Rory's lawn rake rarely rakes really right.

194. Lucky rabbits like to cause a ruckus.

195. Four fine fresh fish for you.

196. She sold six shabby sheared sheep on ship.

197. The top cop saw a cop top.

198. A pessimistic pest exists amidst us.

199. A singly circularly linked list.

200. Aluminum, linoleum, molybdenum, aluminum, linoleum, molybdenum, aluminum, linoleum, molybdenum

201. An illusory vision is a visionary illusion. Is it?

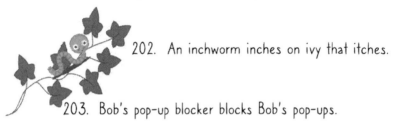

202. An inchworm inches on ivy that itches.

203. Bob's pop-up blocker blocks Bob's pop-ups.

204. Casual clothes are provisional for leisurely trips across Asia.

205. Certified certificates from certified certificate certifiers.

206. Cook "Cookie" Turk took Kookie Kirk a turkey cookie

207. Four poor fools filled four pools full.

208. Fresh fish and fried prawns

209. Frozen Floyd flicks fat fleas for a fixed flat fee.

210. Furnish Freddie's nursery with forty-four furry
Furby Beanie Babies.

211. Green and brown blades of grass

212. He wanted to desert his dessert in the desert!

213. I broke a brickbat and a brickbat broke me.

214. I gratefully gazed at the gracefully grazing gazelles.

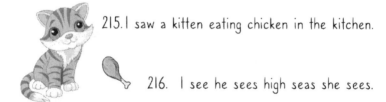

215. I saw a kitten eating chicken in the kitchen.

216. I see he sees high seas she sees.

217. It's a nice night for a white rice fight.

218. I'm perfectly practiced and practically perfect.

219. Lenny Lou leopard led leprechauns leaping like lemmings.

220. Lucid Lou slued loose the sluice that slew the slough.

221. Minsea and Youngsea made this together in their English class.

222. My back black brake blocks are broken.

223. Quick queens quack quick quacks quicker than quacking quails.

224. Rather Ruth's writhings than Roth's wrath.

225. She snapped a selfie with Sophie's silver cell phone.

226. Silly shoe-fly pie fans sell chilly shoe-fly pie pans.

227. This is the sushi chef.

228. Sure, sir, the ship's sure shipshape, sir.

229. Susie sits shinning silver shoes.

230. The children eat the chicken in the kitchen.

231. The greedy Greek geek agreed.

232. Three free fleas flew freely through the flu.

233. Three tired tigers try to throw three trees.

234. Whoever slit the sheets is a good sheet slitter

235. Willy's wooden whistle wouldn't whistle when Willy

went wild.

236. You're behaving like a babbling,

bumbling band of baboons.

237. A tricky frisky snake with sixty super scaly stripes.

238. A pale pink proud peacock pompously preened its

pretty plumage.

239. Eleven owls licked eleven little liquorice lollipops

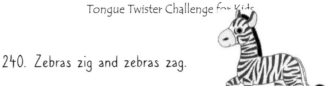

240. Zebras zig and zebras zag.

241. Vivacious Val vacuumed Violet's very vivid

vehicle

242. Eddie edited Earl's easy music.

243. Annie ate eight Arctic apples.

244. Printed papers under pressure

make pens prickle.

245. An awful aardvark and an aching ape ate an antelope.

246. An orange oval spooks the odd operative.

247. The poor boar pours batter over his putter.

248. Shave a single shingle thin.

249. Kindly kittens knitting mittens keep kazooing in the

king's kitchen.

250. Linda-Lou Lambert loves lemon lollipop lip gloss.

251. A shapeless sash sags slowly.

252. Smelly shoes and socks shock sisters.

253. The cat catchers can't catch caught cats.

254. Three fluffy feathers fell

from Phoebe's flimsy fan.

255. She should shun the shinning sun.

256. Little Lillian lets lazy lizards lie along the lily pads.

257. A bragging baker baked black bread.

258. We supply wristwatches for witch-watchers watching

witches Washington wishes watched.

259. Charlie chooses cheese and cherries.

260. Cheerful children chant charming tunes.

261. One must not touch the Dutch too much.

262. The child watched his teacher and fetched
him the chalk.

263. Charles and Richard chewed cheese and chewed gum.

264. Jean, Joan, George and Gerald judged generally.

265. Jolly Jack and joyful Jill jumping down the jagged hill.

266. John Johnson joined jealous Jenny Jerry making
apple-jelly.

267. Reading Bells ring rapidly and reeds rustle round rivers.

268. Rolling on the roaring river the rowing-raft rolled over.

269. As the roaring rocket rose, the restless monsters
rollicked.

270. Strawberries, raspberries and redcurrants with real cream are really refreshing.

271. Seventy-seven sea serpents swam hissing across the sea.

272. Six slippery seals slipping silently ashore.

273. They threw three thick things.

274. Three Scotch thistles in the thicket.

275. The third Thursday of this month is the thirteenth.

276. Wee Willy Winkie went walking in the wet wood.

277. Warm, whispering winds fill woodland waves.

TWISTED

◆ • ◆ • ◆ • ◆ • ◆ • ◆ • ◆

(11 to 20 words)

If Stu chews shoes, should Stu choose the shoes he chews?

1. Fresh fried fish,

    Fish fresh fried, Fried fish fresh, Fish fried fresh.

2. Swan swam over the sea,

    Swim, swan, swim!

    Swan swam back again

    Well swum, swan!

3. I saw Susie sitting in a shoe shine shop.

    Where she sits she shines, and where she shines she sits.

4. I slit a sheet, a sheet I slit, upon a slitted sheet I sit.

5. Lonely lowland llamas are ladylike.

    A tidy tiger tied a tie tighter to tidy her tiny tail.

    A skunk sat on a stump and thunk the stump stunk,

    But the stump thunk the skunk stunk.

6. Washington's wash woman washed Washington's wash while

    Washington's wife went west.

7. Why do you cry, Willy?

   Why do you cry?

   Why, Willy?

   Why, Willy?

   Why, Willy? Why?

8. Denise sees the fleece,

   Denise sees the fleas.

   At least Denise could sneeze

   And feed and freeze the fleas.

9. A big black bug bit a big black dog on his big black

   nose!

10. A sailor went to sea to see

    What he could see

    But all he could see

    Was sea, sea, sea.

11. That fish has a fat fin.

This fish is a fish that

Has a thinner fin than that fish.

12. The thirty-three thieves thought that they thrilled the

throne throughout Thursday.

13. If Stu chews shoes, should Stu choose the shoes he chews?

14. There those thousand thinkers were thinking how did the

other three thieves go through.

15. How much pot, could a pot-roast roast, if a pot roast could

roast pot.

16. She saw Sherif's shoes on the sofa. But was she so sure

she saw Sherif's shoes on the sofa?

17. Rory the warrior and Roger the worrier were reared wrongly in a rural brewery.

18. I stood sadly on the silver steps of Burgess's fish sauce shop, mimicking him hiccupping, and wildly welcoming him within.

19. Rhys watched Ross switch his Irish wristwatch for a Swiss wristwatch.

20. The ruddy widow really wants ripe watermelon and red roses when winter arrives.

21. How many sheets could a sheet slitter slit if a sheet slitter could slit sheets?

22. If you're keen on stunning kites and cunning stunts, buy a cunning stunning stunt kite.

23. Suzie Seaword's fish-sauce shop sells unsifted thistles for thistle-sifters to sift.

24. Wunwun was a racehorse, Tutu was one too.

Wunwun won one race, Tutu won one too

25. The big black bug bit the big black bear,

but the big black bear bit the big black

bug back!

26. Five fuzzy French frogs frolicked through the fields in France.

27. I see a sea down by the seashore.

But which sea do you see down

by the seashore?

28. There once was a two toed, she toad, tree toad, and a three toed,

he toad, tree toad.

29. The owner of the inside inn was inside his inside inn

with his inside outside his inside inn.

30. If you notice this notice,

you will notice that this notice is not worth noticing.

31. There those thousand thinkers were thinking where did those other three thieves go through.

32. I would if I could! But I can't, so I won't!

33. If colored caterpillars could change their colors constantly could they keep their colored coat colored properly?

34. How much ground could a groundhog grind if a groundhog could grind ground?

35. How may saws could a see-saw saw if a see-saw could saw saws?

36. Come, come,

Stay calm, stay calm,

No need for alarm,

It only hums,

It doesn't harm.

37. Tie a knot, tie a knot.

Tie a tight, tight knot.

Tie a knot in the shape of a naught.

38. How much oil boil can a gum boil

if a gum boil can boil oil?

39. I'm a sheet slitter.

I slit sheets.

I'm the sleekest sheet slitter

that ever slit sheets.

40. While we were walking, we were watching window washers

wash Washington's windows with warm washing water.

41. There are two minutes difference from four to two to

two to two, from two to two to two, too.

42. You know New York. You need New York.

You know you need unique New York.

43. Mrs. Hunt had a country cut front

in the front of her country cut petticoat.

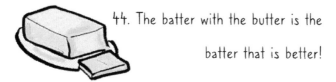

44. The batter with the butter is the

batter that is better!

45. There's a sandwich on the sand which was sent by a sane

witch.

46. How many yaks could a yak-pack pack if a yak pack

could pack yaks?

47. Can you imagine an imaginary menagerie manager imagining

managing an imaginary menagerie?

48. A box of biscuits,

a box of mixed biscuits,

and a biscuit mixer.

49. If two witches would watch two watches, which witch

would watch which watch?

50. A proper cup of coffee from
a proper copper coffee pot.

51. A smart fella, a fella smart.
It takes a smart fella to say a fella smart.

52. Fuzzy Wuzzy was a bear,

Fuzzy Wuzzy had no hair,

Fuzzy Wuzzy wasn't very fuzzy, was he?

53. One black beetle bled only black blood, the other black

beetle bled blue.

54. A skunk sat on a stump and thunk the stump stunk,
but the stump thunk the skunk stunk.

55. Picky people pick Peter Pan Peanut Butter.

Peter Pan Peanut is the peanut picky people pick.

56. The king would sing, about a ring that would go ding.

57. I wish I were what I was when I wished I were what I am.

58. The crow flew over the river with a lump of raw liver.

59. No need to light a night light on a light night like tonight.

60. If you go for a gopher a gopher will go for a gopher hole.

61. Seven slick and sexy sealskin ski suits slid slowly down the slope.

62. Six sick hicks nick six slick bricks with picks and sticks.

63. A haddock! A haddock! A blackspotted haddock! A black spot on the black back of a blackspotted haddock!

64. A pleasant place to place a plaice is a place where a plaice is pleased to be placed.

65. A rough coated, dough faced, thoughtful ploughman strode through the streets of Scarborough; after falling into a slough, he coughed and hiccoughed.

66. Betty and Bob brought back blue balloons from the big bazaar.

67. Cows graze in droves on grass that grows on grooves in groves.

68. Fred Threlfall's thirty-five fine threads are finer threads than Fred Threlfall's thirty-five thick threads.

69. Hassock hassock, black spotted hassock. Black spot on a black back of a black spotted hassock..

70. If I assist a sister assistant, will the sister's sister assistant assist me?

71. I'm not the wood cutter,
I'm the wood cutter's son.
And I'm only cutting wood
Till the wood cutter comes.

72. The lips, the teeth, the tip of the tongue,

the tip of the tongue, the teeth, the lips

73. Love's a feeling you feel when you feel

you're going to feel the feeling you've never felt before.

74. Mares eat oats and does eat oats,

and little lambs eat ivy.

A Kid will eat ivy too, wouldn't you?

75. Meter maid Mary married manly Matthew Marcus

Mayo, a moody male mailman

moving mostly metered mail.

76. My dame hath a lame tame crane, my dame hath a crane

that is lame.

77. Old Mr. Hunt

had a cuddy punt

Not a cuddy punt

but a hunt punt cuddy.

78. One-One was a racehorse.

Two-Two was one, too.

When One-One won one race,

Two-Two won one, too.

79. Peter poked a poker at the piper, so the piper poked pepper at Peter.

80. Pick a partner and practice passing,

for if you pass proficiently,

perhaps you'll play professionally.

81. Ruby Rugby's brother bought and brought her back some rubber baby-buggy bumpers.

82. Sarah sitting in her Chevrolet,

All she does is sits and shifts,

All she does is sits and shifts.

83. Say this sharply, say this sweetly,

Say this shortly, say this softly.

Say this sixteen times in succession.

84. Seven sleazy shysters in sharkskin suits sold sheared

sealskins to seasick sailors.

85. She stood on the balcony, inexplicably mimicking him

hiccupping, and amicably welcoming him in.

86. Suddenly swerving, seven small swans

Swam silently southward,

Seeing six swift sailboats

Sailing sedately seaward.

87. "Surely Sylvia swims!" shrieked Sammy, surprised.

"Someone should show Sylvia some strokes so she shall not

sink."

88. Ten tame tadpoles tucked tightly together in a thin tall tin.

89. Thank the other three brothers of their father's mother's brother's side.

90. The Smothers brothers' father's mother's brothers are the Smothers brothers' mother's father's other brothers.

91. Three gray geese in the green grass grazing. Gray were the geese and green was the grass.

92. Two Truckee truckers truculently truckling to have truck to truck two trucks of truck.

93. Which witch snitched the stitched switch for which the Swiss witch wished?

94. I looked right at Larry's rally and left in a hurry.

95. Thirty-three thousand feathers on a thrushes throat.

96. I have got a date at a quarter to eight; I'll see you at the gate, so don't be late.

97. A maid named Lady Marmalade made mainly lard and lemonade. M'lady lamely never made a well-named, labelled marmalade.

98. Carolina Herrera resides in the rural area with her running horses.

99. Deer, deer, oh dear, oh dear, your career as a deer is over here.

100. Farrell's features fabulous food 'n' fantastic fountain fantasies for frolicking, fun-filled festive families.

101. Frank's fisher fishes on Friday for Frank's Friday fresh fried fish-fest

102. Freddy is ready to roast red roaches. Ready for Freddy's roasted red roaches?

103. Giddy kiddy goat, Giddy kiddy goat,

Giddy, giddy, giddy, giddy, giddy, kiddy goat

104. How many bears could Bear Grills grill if Bear grills

could grill bears?

105. How many boards could the Mongols hoard if the

Mongol hordes got bored?

106. How many cats would a caddie catch if a caddie could

catch cats?

107. How many ducks could a duck duct-tape, if a duck could duct-

tape ducks?

108. How many pounds in a groundhog's mound when a groundhog

pounds hog mounds?

109. How many rats would the ruskies roast if the ruskies could

roast rats?

110. How many snacks could a snack stacker stack, if a snack stacker snacked stacked snacks?

111. How many tow trucks could a tow truck tow if a tow truck could tow tow trucks?

112. How much cash could a sasquatch stash if a sasquatch could stash cash?

113. How much snus could a moose on the loose use if a moose on the loose could use loose snus?

114. How much squash could a sasquatch squish, if a sasquatch could squish squash?

115. It's not right to write Wright 'Rite', please try to write Wright right!

116. Ken can ken that Ken's kin can ken Ken's kin's ken.

117. Of all the vids I've ever viewed, I've never viewed a vid as valued as Arvi's vid.

118. Sweet sagacious Sally Sanders said she sure saw seven segregated seaplanes sailing swiftly southward Saturday.

119. Tell Tom the ticket taker to take the ticket to the ticket wicket.

120. They hatch fish at the state fish hatchery and sell hatched fish to the fish stick factory.

121. They think that their teeth get thinner at times they want to taste thick meat.

122. Thomas Tattamus took two T's to tie two tots to two tall trees.

123. Thrifty Theophilus, the theocratic thistle sifter, thrice thrust three thousand thistles through the slick thick of his softly throbbing thumb.

124. Washing the washing machine while watching the washing machine washing.

125. I can think of six thin things, but I can think of six thick things too.

126. The big bug bit the little beetle, but the little beetle bit the big bug back.

127. A rhinoceros rushed into a restaurant and ordered ribs of beef, rabbit, rolls, raspberries, radishes, rhubarb pie and rice.

128. If you want to buy, buy, if you don't want to buy, bye bye!

129. Super-duper storm troopers whoop it up at Death Star groupers: helmet thrashing, rebel bashing, laser blasting at party poopers.

130. Brisk brave brigadiers brandished broad bright blades, blunderbusses, and bludgeons balancing them badly.

131. Charles is a cheerful chicken-farmer. He chuckles at the chance Of a choice chicken to chew for his lunch.

132. Jane and Jenny in their blue jackets are watching the jaguar in the cage.

133. It was a joy for Jack and George, the German boys, to cross the large bridge before entering the village.

134. Rustle of trees and ripple of rain, roaring of rivers across the plain.

135. Seventeen slimy slugs in satin sunbonnets sat singing short, sad songs.

136. If practice makes perfect and perfect needs practice, I'm perfectly practiced and practically perfect.

DOUBLE KNOT

(more than 20 words)

How much dew does a dewdrop drop if dewdrops do drop dew?

1. William always wears a very warm

    Woolen vest in winter.

    Victor however will never wear

    Underwear even in the wild west.

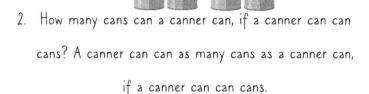

2. How many cans can a canner can, if a canner can can

    cans? A canner can can as many cans as a canner can,

    if a canner can can cans.

3. How much wood would a woodchuck chuck

    If a woodchuck could chuck wood?

    He would chuck, he would,

    as much as he could,

    And chuck as much as a woodchuck would

    If a woodchuck could chuck wood.

4. Once a fellow met a fellow in a field of beans. Said

    a fellow to a fellow, "If a fellow asks a fellow, Can a

    fellow tell a fellow what a fellow means?"

5. She sells seashells by the seashore.

The shells she sells are surely seashells.

So if she sells shells on the seashore,

I'm sure she sells seashore shells.

6. Whether the weather be fine

Or whether the weather be not

Whether the weather be cold

Or whether the weather be hot

We'll weather the weather whatever the weather

Weather we like it or not.

7. Pussycat, pussycat

Can you catch that bad fat rat?

If you catch that bad fat rat,

You will have some milk for that.

8. Peter Piper picked a peck of
pickled peppers. Did Peter Piper
pick a peck of pickled peppers?
If Peter Piper picked a peck of pickled
peppers, Where's the peck of pickled peppers Peter Piper picked?

9. I can think of six thin things

-Six thin things?

Can you think?

-Yes, I can think of six thin things too.

10. A bad man sat on my hat

In the tram, he is a bad man

That man. That's fact. I'm glad

I had a bag in my hand

Or he would have sat on that.

11. A twister of twists once twisted a twist;

A twist that he twisted was a three-twisted twist;

If in twisting a twist one twist should untwist,

The untwisted twist would untwist the twist.

12. There was a fisherman named Fisher
who fished for some fish in a fissure.
Till a fish with a grin,
pulled the fisherman in.
Now they're fishing the fissure for Fisher.

13. How many cookies could a good cook cook If a good cook could cook cookies?   A good cook could cook as much cookies as a good cook who could cook cookies.

14. How much ground would a groundhog hog, if a groundhog could hog ground?   A groundhog would hog all the ground he could hog, if a groundhog could hog ground.

15. How much caramel can a canny cannonball cram in a camel if a canny cannonball can cram caramel in a camel?

16. Through three cheese trees three free fleas flew.

    While these fleas flew, freezy breeze blew.

    Freezy breeze made these three trees freeze.

    Freezy trees made these trees' cheese freeze.

    That's what made these three free fleas sneeze.

17. I wish to wish the wish you wish to wish, but if you wish the wish the witch wishes, I won't wish the wish you wish to wish.

18. Yellow butter, purple jelly, red jam, black bread. Spread it thick, say it quick! Yellow butter, purple jelly, red jam, black bread. Spread it thicker, say it quicker! Yellow butter, purple jelly, red jam, black bread. Don't eat with your mouth full!

19. If you can't can any candy can,

    how many candy cans can a candy canner can

    if he can can candy cans?

20. I saw a saw in Arkansas,

that would outsaw any saw I ever saw,

and if you got a saw

that will outsaw the saw I saw in Arkansas,

let me see your saw.

21. Sister Suzie sewing shirts for soldiers

Such skill as sewing shirts

Our shy young sister Suzie shows

Some soldiers send epistles

Say they'd rather sleep in thistles

Than the saucy, soft short shirts for soldiers Sister Suzie sews.

22. Knife and a fork bottle and a cork

that is the way you spell New York.

Chicken in the car and the car can go,

that is the way you spell Chicago.

23. As he gobbled the cakes on his plate,

the greedy ape said as he ate,

the greener green grapes are,

the keener keen apes

are to gobble green

grape cakes,

they're great!

24. How much myrtle would a wood turtle hurdle if a wood

turtle could hurdle myrtle?

A wood turtle would hurdle as much myrtle as a wood turtle

could hurdle if a wood turtle could hurdle myrtle.

25. A fly and flea flew into a flue,

said the fly to the flea 'what shall we do?'

'let us fly' said the flea

said the fly 'shall we flee'

so they flew through a flaw in the flue.

26. How much dew does a dewdrop drop

If dewdrops do drop dew?

They do drop, they do

As do dewdrops drop

If dewdrops do drop dew.

27. If Kantie can tie a tie and untie a tie,

why can't I tie a tie and untie a tie like Kantie can.

28. Mr. Tongue Twister tried to train his tongue to twist and turn, and

twit an twat, to learn the letter ""T""

29. A lady sees a pot-mender at work at his barrow in the street.

""Are you copper-bottoming them, my man?""

""No, I'm aluminiuming 'em, Mum""

30. I am not a pheasant plucker,

I'm a pheasant plucker's son

but I'll be plucking pheasants

When the pheasant plucker's gone.

31. Pete's pa Pete poked to the pea patch to pick

    a peck of peas for the

    poor pink pig

    in the pine hole pig-pen.

32. Suzie, Suzie, working in a shoeshine shop.

    All day long she sits and shines,

    all day long she shines and sits,

    and sits and shines, and shines and sits,

    and sits and shines, and shines and sits.

    Suzie, Suzie, working in a shoeshine shop.

33. Tommy, Tommy, toiling in a tailor's shop.

    All day long he fits and tucks,

    all day long he tucks and fits,

    and fits and tucks, and tucks and fits,

    and fits and tucks, and tucks and fits.

    Tommy, Tommy, toiling in a tailor's shop.

34. There once was a man who had a sister, his name was Mr. Fister. Mr. Fister's sister sold sea shells by the sea shore. Mr. Fister didn't sell sea shells, he sold silk sheets. Mr. Fister told his sister that he sold six silk sheetsto six shieks. The sister of Mr. Fister said Isold six shells to six shieks too!

35. An undertaker undertook to undertake an undertaking. The undertaking that the undertaker undertook was the hardest undertaking the undertaker ever undertook to undertake.

36. When a doctor doctors a doctor, does the doctor doing the doctoring doctor as the doctor being doctored wants to be doctored or does the doctor doing the doctoring doctor as he wants to doctor?

37. She is a thistle-sifter. She has a sieve of unsifted thistles and a sieve of sifted thistles and the sieve of unsifted thistles she sifts into the sieve of sifted thistles because she is a thistle-sifter.

38. Admidst the mists and coldest frosts,

With stoutest wrists and loudest boasts,

He thrusts his fists against the posts,

And still insists he sees the ghosts.

39. King Thistle stuck a thousand thistles in the thistle of his thumb.

A thousand thistles King Thistle stuck in the thistle

of his thumb If King Thistle stuck a

thousand thistles in the thistle of his

thumb, How many thistles did King Thistle

stick in the thistle of his thumb?

40. The bottle of perfume that Willy sent

was highly displeasing to Millicent.

Her thanks were so cold

that they quarreled, I'm told o'er that silly

scent Willy sent Millicent.

41. Three tree turtles took turns talking tongue twisters. If three tree turtles took turns talking tongue twisters, where's the twisters the three tree turtles talked?

42. I thought a thought.

But the thought I thought wasn't the thought I thought I thought.

If the thought I thought I thought had been the thought I thought,

I wouldn't have thought so much.

43. How much dough would Bob Dole dole

if Bob Dole could dole dough?

Bob Dole would dole as much dough

as Bob Dole could dole,

if Bob Dole could dole dough.

44. Ray Rag ran across a rough road.

Across a rough road Ray Rag ran.

Where is the rough road Ray Rag ran across?

45. If Pickford's packers packed a packet of crisps would the packet of crisps that Pickford's packers packed survive for two and a half years?

46. A tooter who tooted a flute Tried to tutor two tutors to toot. Said the two to the tutor, "Is it harder to toot or To tutor two tutors to toot?"

47. A maid with a duster

Made a furious bluster

Dusting a bust in the hall.

When the bust that was dusted The bust that was busted, The bust it was dust, that's all.

48. Mrs. Puggy Wuggy has a square cut punt.

Not a punt cut square,

Just a square cut punt.

It's round in the stern and blunt in the front.

Mrs. Puggy Wuggy has a square cut punt.

49. As I went into the garden

I saw five brave maids

Sitting on five broad beds

Braiding broad braids.

I said to these five brave maids

Sitting on five broad beds

Braiding broad braids, "Braid broad braids, brave maids

50. Birdie birdie in the sky laid a turdie in my eye.

If cows could fly, I'd have a cow pie in my eye.

51. A bitter biting bittern

Bit a better brother bittern,

And the bitter better bittern

Bit the bitter biter back.

And the bitter bittern, bitten,

By the better bitten bittern,

Said: "I'm a bitter biter bit, alack!"

52. A woman to her son did utter, "Go my son, and shut
the shutter." "The shutter's shut," the son did utter,
"I cannot shut it any shutter."

53. Bill had a billboard.
`Bill also had a board bill.
The board bill bored Bill,
So Bill sold his billboard
And paid his board bill.

Then the board bill
No longer bored Bill,
But though he had no board bill,
Neither did he have his billboard!

54. How many berries could a bare berry carry,

if a bare berry could carry berries?

Well they can't carry berries

(which could make you very wary)

but a bare berry carried is more scary!

55. I need not your needles, they're needless to me;

For kneading of noodles, 'twere needless, you see;

But did my neat knickers but need to be kneed,

I then should have need of your needles indeed.

56. I wish to wish, I dream to dream, I try to try, and I

live to live, and I'd die to die, and I cry to cry

but I don't know why.

57. If a packet hits a pocket on a socket on a port,

And the bus is interrupted as a very last resort,

And the address of the memory makes your floppy disk

abort, Then the socket packet pocket has an error to

report!

58. If you must cross a course cross cow across a crowded cow crossing, cross the cross coarse cow across the crowded cow crossing carefully

59. If you saw a pinky, pug puppy playing ping pong with a pig.or a great grey goose a'golfing with a goat, . would you think it half as funny as a big brown Belgian bunny blowing bubbles with a bishop in a boat?

60. If you understand, say ""understand"".
If you don't understand,
say ""don't understand"".
But if you understand and
say ""don't understand"".
How do I understand that you understand? Understand!?

61. To begin to toboggan first buy a toboggan, but don't buy too big a toboggan. Too big a toboggan is too big a toboggan to buy to begin to toboggan.

62. If your cursor finds a menu item followed by a dash,

And the double-clicking icon puts your window in the trash,

And your data is corrupted 'cause the index doesn't hash,

then your situation's hopeless, and your system's gonna crash!

63. Moses supposes his toeses are roses,

but Moses supposes erroneously.

For Moses, he knowses his toeses aren't roses,

as Moses supposes his toeses to be.

64. Luke's duck likes lakes. Luke Luck licks lakes. Luke's duck

licks lakes. Duck takes licks in

lakes Luke Luck likes. Luke Luck takes licks in lakes duck

likes.

65. Which witch switched the Swiss wristwatches?

66. Theophilus Thadeus Thistledown, the successful
thistle-sifter, while sifting a sieve-full of
unsifted thistles, thrust three thousand thistles through
the thick of his thumb.
Now, if Theophilus Thadeus Thistledown, the successful
thistle-sifter, thrust three thousand thistles
through the thick of his thumb, see that thou, while sifting a
sieve-full of unsifted thistles, thrust not three thousand thistles
through the thick of thy thumb.

67. Of all the felt I ever felt,
I never felt a piece of felt
which felt as fine as that felt felt,
when first I felt that felt hat's felt.

68. Oh, the sadness of her sadness when she's sad.

Oh, the gladness of her gladness when she's glad.

But the sadness of her sadness,

and the gladness of her gladness,

Are nothing like her madness when she's mad!

69. On mules we find two legs behind

and two we find before.

We stand behind before we find

what those behind be for.

70. Our Joe wants to know if your Joe will lend our Joe your Joe's banjo. If your Joe won't lend our Joe your Joe's banjo, our Joe won't lend your Joe our Joe's banjo when our Joe has a banjo!

71. Pretty Kitty Creighton had a cotton batten cat.

The cotton batten cat was bitten by a rat.

The kitten that was bitten had a button for an eye,

And biting off the button made the cotton batten fly.

72. Sarah saw a shot-silk sash shop full of shot-silk sashes

as the sunshine shone on the side of the shot-silk sash shop.

73. Sheila is selling her shop at the seashore,

For shops at the seashore are so sure to lose.

Now she's not so sure of what she should be selling!

Should Sheila sell seashells or should she sell shoes?

74. Silly Sally swiftly shooed seven silly sheep.

The seven silly sheep Silly Sally shooed

shilly-shallied south.

These sheep shouldn't sleep in a shack.

sheep should sleep in a shed.

75. Shop chat my shop stocks: locks, chips, chopsticks, watch straps,

traps, tops, taps, tricks, ship's clocks, lipstick and chimney pots.

What does your shop stock? Sharkskin socks.

76. Terry Teeter, a teeter-totter teacher, taught her daughter Tara

to teeter-totter, but Tara Teeter didn't teeter-totter as Terry

Teeter taught her to.

77. Something in a thirty-acre thermal thicket of thorns and thistles

thumped and thundered

threatening the three-D thoughts of Matthew the thug - although,

theatrically, it was only the

thirteen-thousand thistles and thorns through the underneath of

his thigh that the thirty year

old thug thought of that morning.

78. Richard is in the kitchen fetching some cheese for the

children; Rose has two red rulers from her friend in her room.

79. Susan shineth shoes and socks;

socks and shoes shines Susan.

She ceased shining shoes and socks,

for shoes and socks shock Susan.

80. Swim, Sam, swim.

Show them you are some swimmer. Swim like the snow-white

swan swam.

A well swum swim is a swim well swum.

So, swim, Sam. Swim!

81. The twain that in twining before in the twine,

As twines were intwisted he now doth untwine;

Twist the twain inter-twisting a twine more

between,

He, twirling his twister, makes a twist of the twine.

82. Hercules, a hardy hunter, hunted a hare in the Hampshire Hills.

Hit him on the head with a hard, hard hammer and he howled

horribly!

83. Yally Bally had a jolly golliwog. Feeling folly, Yally Bally

Bought his jolly golli' a dollie made of

holly! The golli', feeling jolly, named the holly dollie,

Polly. So Yally Bally's jolly golli's holly

dollie Polly's also jolly!

84. Dr. Johnson and Mr. Johnson, after great consideration, came to the conclusion that the Indian nation beyond the Indian Ocean is back in education because the chief occupation is cultivation.

85. Breakfast for one

Hot thick crusty buttery toast

Buttery toasty thick hot crust

Crusty buttery hot thick toast

Crusty thick hot toasty butter

Thick hot buttery crusty toast

Toasty buttery hot thick crust

Hot buttery thick crusty toast –

With marmalade is how I like it most!

86. A wooden worm wouldn't be worthy of worship but would he if he wondered and worried about what he would be worthy of if he wasn't wooden?

87. Chester chooses chestnuts, cheddar cheese with chewy chives.
He chews them and he chooses them. He chooses them and he
chews them Those chestnuts, cheddar cheese and chives in
cheery, charming chunks.

88. Colliding, colt riding cowboys,
combining colliding while gliding at night coinciding in their fight.
It wasn't quite trite even with slight sight, who was right? The fight
like light, flashed bright, fast as bears bite flies flying near the
bears eyes the fleeing flies die.

89. Grandma Gabby Grammer grabbed a gram of gummy
goulash.
If Grandma Gabby Grammer grabbed a gram of gummy
goulash,
How many grams of gummy goulash did Grandma Gabby
Grammer grab?

90. They have left the thrift shop, and lost both their theatre tickets and the volume of valuable licenses and coupons for free theatrical frills and thrills.

91. How many wenches could a witch's wench wrench wrench if a witch's wench wrench could wrench wenches? As many wenches as a witch's wench wrench could, if a witch's wench wrench could wrench wenches.

92. How much juice does a fruit juice producer produce when a fruit juice producer produces fruit juice? We can deduce a fruit juice produces as much juice as a fruit juice produce can seduce from the fruit that produces juice.

93. I feel a feel a funny feel a funny feel feel I,
If I feel a funny feel a funny feel feel I.

94. If your Bob doesn't give our Bob that bob that your Bob owes our Bob, our Bob will give your Bob a bob in the eye.

95. Tricky Tristan tracked a trail of tiny turtles.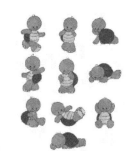

How many tiny turtles did Tricky Tristan track?

Tricky Tristan tracked twenty-two tiny turtles;

that's how many tiny turtles tricky Tristan tracked.

96. Now the trees are all groaning in growling, rough gales that with

thuds and hoarse roaring roll raging around!

Such leaf-rousing, branch-ruining, ripping, raw wails, such a

terrible, thrashing and tree-wrecking sound!

97. A right-handed fellow named Wright,

In writing 'write' always wrote 'rite'

Where he meant to write right.

If he'd written 'write' right

Wright would not have wrought rot writing 'rite.'

98. Slinking, sliding, slithering slyly,

Swiftly slipping through the grasses shyly,

Silent but for swish and hiss

Is the sinuous snake's leglessness.

99. Tell a tall tale of a tall tailed dog, that told Tim it tap a tall ale and thump the top of Tim's tomb.

100. Silly Sally Shouldnort shaved sheep she should show soon so selling sheep shaved showed she shouldn't show shaved sheep so soon.

101. Which Witch snitched the Snitch Witch? Or did the Snitch Witch snitch the Witch? If the Snitch Witch snitched the Witch then which Witch did the Snitch Witch snitch?

102. You name it, we claim it. If we can't get it, we'll send you to get it. If we can't send you to get it, forget it. Who's got it, if we don't got it?

103. I often sit and think and fish and sit and fish and think and sit and fish - and think - and wish that I could get a fish.

104. I was looking back
To see if she was looking back
To see if I was looking back
To see if she was looking back at me.

105. Whether the weather is warm, whether the weather is hot, we have to put up with the weather, whether we like it or not.

106. Did Dick Pickens prick his pinkie pickling cheap cling peaches in an inch of Pinch or framing his famed French finch photos?

107. Sammy Smellie smelt a smell of small-coal: Did Sammy Smellie smell a smell of small-coal?
If Sammy Smellie smelt a smell of small-coal,
Where's the smell of small-coal Sammy Smellie smelt?

108. Rumbling in the chimneys, rattling at the doors,

Round the roofs and round the roads the rude wind

roars,

Raging through the darkness, raving through the trees,

Racing off again across the great, grey seas.

109. Mrs. Chip is very old,

and when she settles down to stitch

Unless she uses spectacles

she cannot see which stitch is which.

110. Serenity

Mystic moonlight, moments meet

Softly, somewhere songbirds sweet

Simple, soothing, soulful sounds

Mem'ries murmer, mossy mound

Wander wistful, winding ways

Linger, loving, lilacs lay

Lazy langour, listless leaves

Weeping willow, wonder weaves

Pausing, picture, pristine plain

Ruling romance, restive reign

Rising rapture, rustic ride

Perfect pleasure, peace presides.

SUPERCALI-TWISTED

(more than 50 words)

I bought a bit of baking powder and baked a batch of biscuits.

1. Betty Botter bought some butter but she said the butter's

   bitter.

   If I put it in my batter it will make my batter bitter.

   So, she bought some better butter,

   better than the bitter butter

   and she put it in her batter

   and her batter was not bitter.

   So 'twas good that Betty Botter

   bought some better butter

2. Out in the pasture the nature watcher watches the catcher.

   While the catcher watches the pitcher who pitches the balls.

   Whether the temperature's up or whether the temperature's down,

   the nature watcher, the catcher and the pitcher are always around.

   The pitcher pitches, the catcher catches and the watcher watches.

   So whether the temperature's rises or whether the temperature

   falls the nature watcher just watches the catcher who's watching

   the pitcher who's watching the balls.

3.   Esau Wood sawed wood. All the wood Esau Wood saw, Esau
   Wood would saw. All the wood Wood saw, Esau sought to saw.
   One day Esau Wood's wood-saw would saw no wood. So Esau
   Wood sought a new wood-saw. The new wood-saw would saw
   wood. Oh, the wood Esau Wood would saw. Esau sought a saw
   that would saw wood as no other wood-saw would saw. And Esau
   found a saw that would saw as no other wood-saw would saw.
   And Esau Wood sawed wood.

4.   Mr. Inside went over to see Mr. Outside. Mr. Inside stood
   outside and called to Mr. Outside inside. Mr. Outside
   answered Mr. Inside from inside and Told Mr. Inside to come
   inside. Mr. Inside said "NO", and told Mr. Outside to come
   outside. Mr. Outside and Mr. Inside argued from inside and
   outside about going outside or coming inside. Finally, Mr.
   Outside coaxed Mr. Inside to come inside, then both Mr.
   Outside and Mr. Inside went outside to the riverside.

5. A big black bear ate a big black bug. A big black bear sat on a big black bug. A big black bug bit a big black bear and made the big black bear bleed blood. A big black bug bit a big black dog on his big black nose! A big bug bit a bold bald bear and the bold bald bear bled blood badly.

6. If a Hottentot taught a Hottentot tot
To talk ere the tot could totter, Ought the Hottenton tot Be taught to say aught, or naught,...

Or what ought to be taught her? If to hoot and to toot a Hottentot tot Be taught by her Hottentot tutor, Ought the tutor get hot If the Hottentot tot Hoot and toot at her Hottentot tutor?

7. Can you can a canned can into an un-canned can like a canner can can a canned can into an un-canned can?

8. Bobby Bippy bought a bat.Bobby Bippy bought a ball.

With his bat Bob banged the ballBanged it bump against the wall

But so boldly Bobby banged it

That he burst his rubber ball""Boo!""

cried Bobby Bad luck ball

Bad luck Bobby, bad luck ball

Now to drown his many troubles

Bobby Bippy's blowing bubbles.

9. A tree toad loved a she-toad Who lived up in a tree. He was

a two-toed tree toad. But a three-toed toad was she.

The two-toed tree toad tried to win. The three-toed she-

toad's heart, For the two-toed tree toad loved the ground

That the three-toed tree toad trod.

But the two-toed tree toad tried in vain. He couldn't please

her whim. From her tree toad bower

With her three-toed power. The she-toad vetoed him.

10. He's the Twistable Turnable Squeezable Pullable Stretchable

Foldable Man. He can crawl in your pocket or fit your locket

Or screw himself into a twenty-volt socket,

Or stretch himself up to the steeple or taller,

Or squeeze himself into a thimble or smaller,

Yes he can, course he can,

He's the Twistable Turnable Squeezable Pullable Stretchable

Shrinkable Man. And he lives a passable life

With his Squeezable Lovable Kissable Hugable

Pullable Tugable Wife. And they have two twistable kids

Who bend up the way that they did. And they turn and they

stretch]ust as much as they can. For this Bendable Foldable

Do-what-you're-toldable Easily moldable

Buy-what you're-soldable Washable Mendable

Highly Dependable Buyable Saleable

Always available Bounceable Shakeable

Almost unbreakable Twistable Turnable Man.

11. I bought a bit of baking powder and baked a batch of biscuits. I brought a big basket of biscuits back to the bakery and baked a basket of big biscuits.

Then I took the big basket of biscuits and the basket of big biscuits and mixed the big biscuits with the basket of biscuits that was next to the big basket and put a bunch of biscuits from the basket into a biscuit mixer and brought the basket of biscuits and the box of mixed biscuits and the biscuit mixer to the bakery and opened a tin of sardines.

12. If the label on the cable on the table at your house, says the network is connected to the button on your mouse,

But your packets want to tunnel on another protocol, that's repeatedly rejected by the printer down the hall,

And your screen is all distorted by the side effects of gauss,

So your icons in the window are as wavy as a souse,

Then you may as well reboot and go out with a bang,

'Cause as sure as I'm a poet, the it's gonna hang!

13. Mr. See and Mr. Soar were old friends.
See owned a saw and Soar owned a seesaw. Now See's saw sawed
Soar's seesaw before Soar saw See, which made Soar sore.
Had Soar seen See's saw before See saw Soar's seesaw, then See's
saw would not have sawed Soar's seesaw.
But See saw Soar's seesaw before Soar saw See's saw so See's
saw sawed Soar's seesaw. It was a shame to let
See see Soar so sore because
See's saw sawed Soar's
seesaw.

14. This is a story about four people named Everybody,
Somebody, Anybody and Nobody. There was an important
job to be done and Everybody was sure that Somebody
would do it. Anybody could have done it, but Nobody did it.
Somebody got angry about that, because it was Everybody's
job. Everybody thought Anybody could do it, but Nobody
realized that Everybody wouldn't do it. It ended up that
Everybody blamed Somebody, when Nobody did, what
Anybody could have done.

15. Once upon a barren moor

There dwelt a bear, also a boar,

The bear could not bear the boar,

The bear thought the boar was a bore.

At last the bear could bear no more

That boar that bored him on the moor.

And so one morn he bored the boar—

That boar will bore no more!

16. You've no need to light a night-light

On a light night like tonight,

For a night-light's light's a slight light,

And tonight's a night that's light.

When a night's light, like tonight's light,

It is really not quite right

To light night-lights with their slight lights

On a light night like tonight.

17. One smart fellow, he felt smart. Two smart fellows, they felt smart. Three smart fellows, they felt smart. Four smart fellows, they felt smart. Five smart fellows, they felt smart. Six smart fellows, they felt smart. Seven smart fellows, they felt smart. Eight smart fellows, they felt smart. Nine smart fellows, they felt smart. Ten smart fellows, they felt smart!

18. To sit in solemn silence in a dull, dark dock,

In a pestilential prison, with a life-long lock,

Awaiting the sensation of a short, sharp shock,

From a cheap and chippy chopper on a big black block!

A dull, dark dock, a life-long lock,

A short, sharp shock, a big black block!

To sit in solemn silence in a pestilential prison,

And awaiting the sensation

From a cheap and chippy chopper on a big black block!

19. Six Pink Minks And Finks

six pink minks think finks stink six finks think pink minks stink six minks in creeks with finks stink if six pink minks pick stinking ink finks if six pink minks had six sticks with six pink ink finks in six creeks then six minks and six finks would have sixty six pink minks and six ink finks then sixty six pink minks and sixty six ink finks would make six ink finks stink cause six pink minks make finks stink.

20. Give me the gift of a grip-top sock, A clip drape shipshape tip top sock. Not your spinslick slapstick slipshod stock, But a plastic, elastic grip-top sock. None of your fantastic slack swap slop From a slap dash flash cash haberdash shop. Not a knick knack knitlock knockneed knickerbocker sock With a mock-shot blob-mottled trick-ticker top clock. Not a supersheet seersucker rucksack sock, Not a spot-speckled frog-freckled cheap sheik's sock Off a hodge-podge moss-blotched scotch- botched block. Nothing slipshod drip drop flip flop or glip glop Tip me to a tip top grip top sock

21. The third time the three three-toed tree toads tried tying their toes together, the third three-toed tree toad tied the two three-toed tree toads toes to the third toads toes. Then the two tied three-toed tree toads told the third three-toed tree toad that tying their toes together thrilled them to their toe tips.

22. Caterpillar catnapping, caught in cocoon

Silently sleeping, seeking sunlit sky

Awake, aware, and awing at atmosphere

Last leaving his lodging, little larva leaps

Spreading his sprouting wings, sailing so skillfully

Wandering with wonder of the whirling world

Lost amid light lilies, he lies

Illuminated in indigo, imagination stirs

Dreams of dancing delightfully in daffodils

Moon moves beneath massive mountains

Sun slides into celestial ceiling

Beautiful butterfly so bubbly and bouncing

Colorful and cleverly casting his charm.

THE TOUGHEST

(It isn't the longest, but it's the hardest)

Try to say it 10 times. You got this!

According to the Guinness Book of World Records, the toughest tongue twister is....

The sixth sick sheik's sixth sheep's sick.

However, researchers from the Massachusetts of Technology say that the most difficult is....

Pad kid poured curd pulled cod.

THE MOST TREASURED CUSTOMER YOU!

The Laughing Lion hopes you enjoyed the book!

As the Lion was writing it, he imagined how happy you'd be with the finished book.

How you'd jump for joy when you received it in the post.

How you'd write in your journal that it's the best book on the planet!

How you'd pass it onto your children for generations to come.

If you did enjoy the book, please take 20 seconds to leave a review.

The Laughing Lion loves reading all the happy moments his books spark.

Wishing you many more joyous moments!

Laughing Lion

Made in the USA
Columbia, SC
27 November 2021

49855908R00070